THIS BOOK BELONGS TO:

B. Valentine Books can arrange author visits for your organization.
Learn more at sarahwbooks.com.

The illustrations in this book were created using the Procreate iPad app.
ISBN 978-0692131770

Fifty percent of profits will be donated to a charity that helps people recover from traumatic brain injuries.

A Spectacular Birdie

By Sarah Warren   Illustrated by Neil Fasen

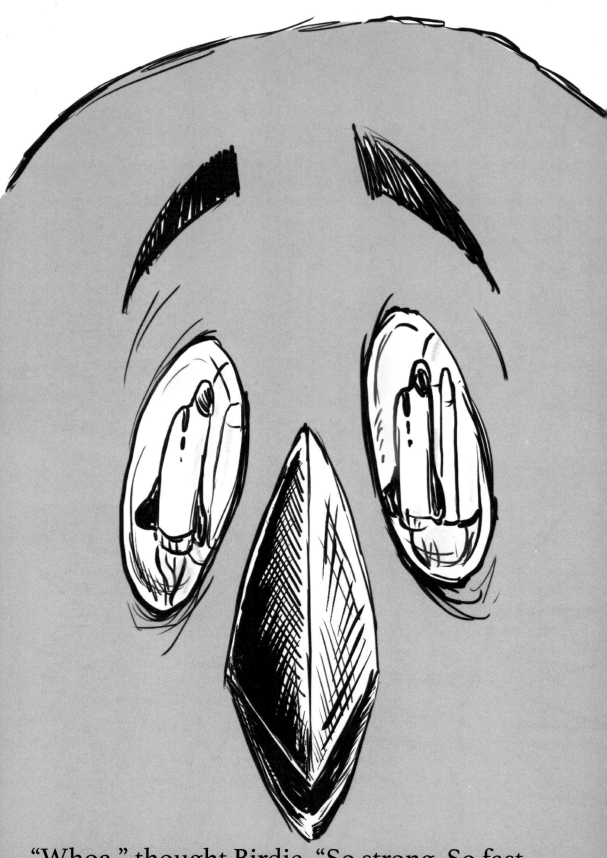

"Whoa," thought Birdie. "So strong. So fast.
So high in the sky. Spectacular! That's a Super Bird

Too late.

Being super might take some practice.

Birdie got to work.

She flapped.

She dove.

She pecked.

She gripped.

She mapped the sky.

Parrot paced.

Birdie didn't hear. She was too busy.

FLAP.

DIVE.

PECK.

GRIP.

Birdie didn't hear. She was having too much fun.

FLAP.

DIVE.

PECK.

GRIP.

Then one night Birdie heard

SLiiiiDE....

SSSSHHHHH.....

and a door clicking sh

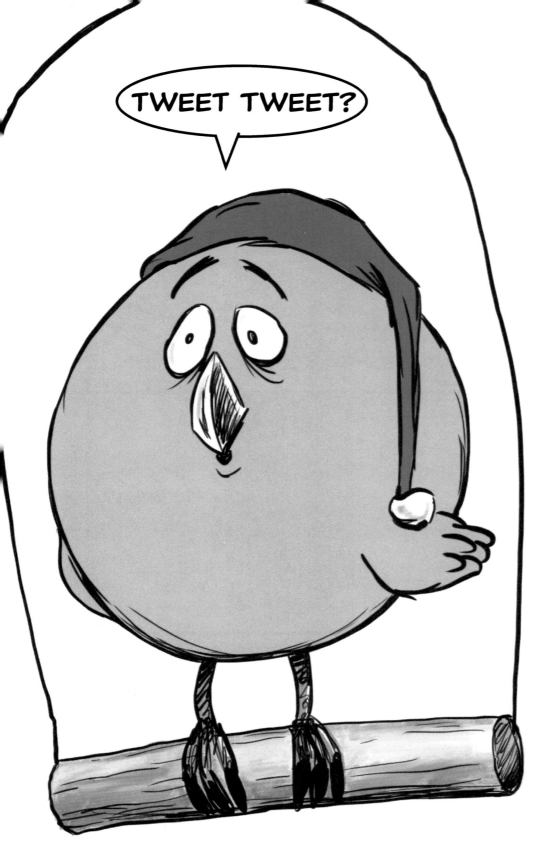

Parrot was never this quiet.

Parrot needed he
Parrot needed...

a SUPER BIRDIE!

Birdie stretched her wings. 3, 2, 1...

Birdie heard every word.

Birdie flapped.

She dove.

She pecked.

She studied the sky.

Once upon a beautiful summer day, Brian and his friends skipped work to play golf. That game gave them a spectacular idea...

Birdies4Brains organizes a very special yearly tournament. Golfers play 100 holes in a single day. Their goal? To raise money for people recovering from traumatic brain injuries. Talk about good sports!

Birdies4Brains founder Brian Eder was inspired by his sister's recovery from an aneurysm. He made it his mission to support other families in similar circumstances. You can join the game or sponsor a golfer. Find out more at b4bmn.org.

Made in the USA
Columbia, SC
17 April 2019